The Jet Pack

New
Vocabulary

Helmet

Just Right Reader Inc.

A jet pack is here!

1

My red jet pack is on.

My helmet is on.

I am on the bed.

I am set!

No!!!

I fell?!

5

I bet it will go if I beg it . . .

7

Will it go if my leg

kicks it?

9

Meg taps it on.

11

Yes!

A B C D Target Phonics Skill

Short /ĕ/ CVC Words

Segmenting Fun

- Tap out the sounds in each word to help your reader learn to spell the word.
- Tap your shoulder for the first sound.
- Tap your elbow for the vowel sound.
- Tap your wrist for the final consonant sound.
- Then, write each letter to spell the word!

Decodable Words

bed	fell	Meg	yes
beg	jet	red	yet
bet	leg	set	

High-Frequency Words

here

Decodable Words can be sounded out based on the letter-sound relationships.

High-Frequency Words are the most commonly used words. Your reader will begin to recognize them.

CVC Words are consonant-vowel-consonant words, like cap or big. The vowel sound is always short.